£3.30

BEANO
TOWN
POLICE
STATION

DE
ME
B

Printed and Published by D. C. THOMSON & Co., LTD.,
185 Fleet Street, London, EC4A 2HS.
© D. C. THOMSON & CO., LTD., 1990.
ISBN 0 85116 485 4

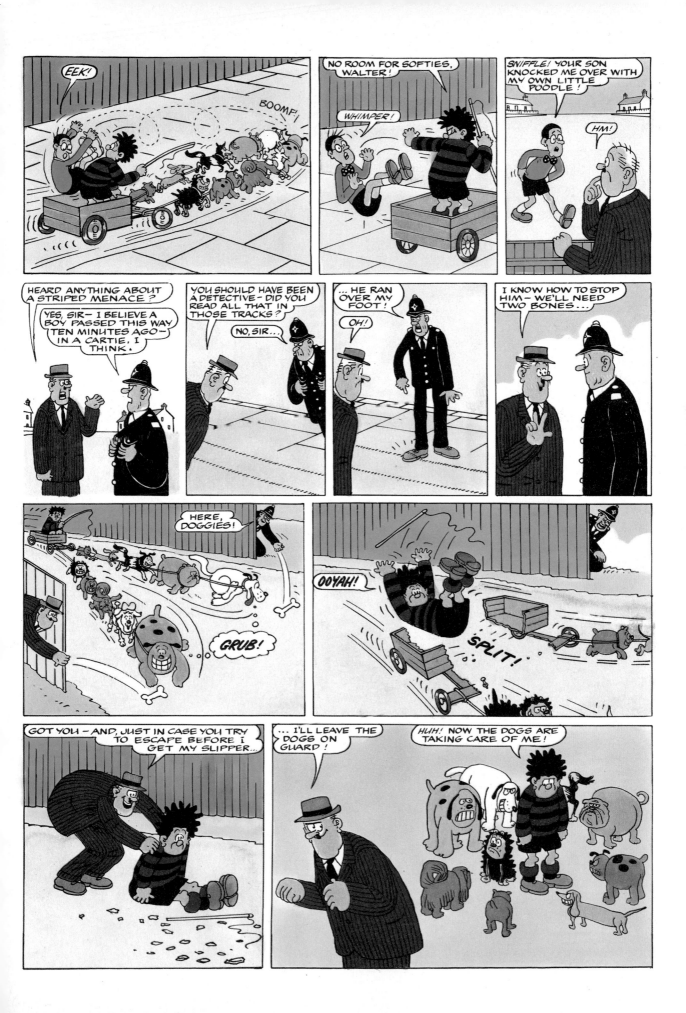

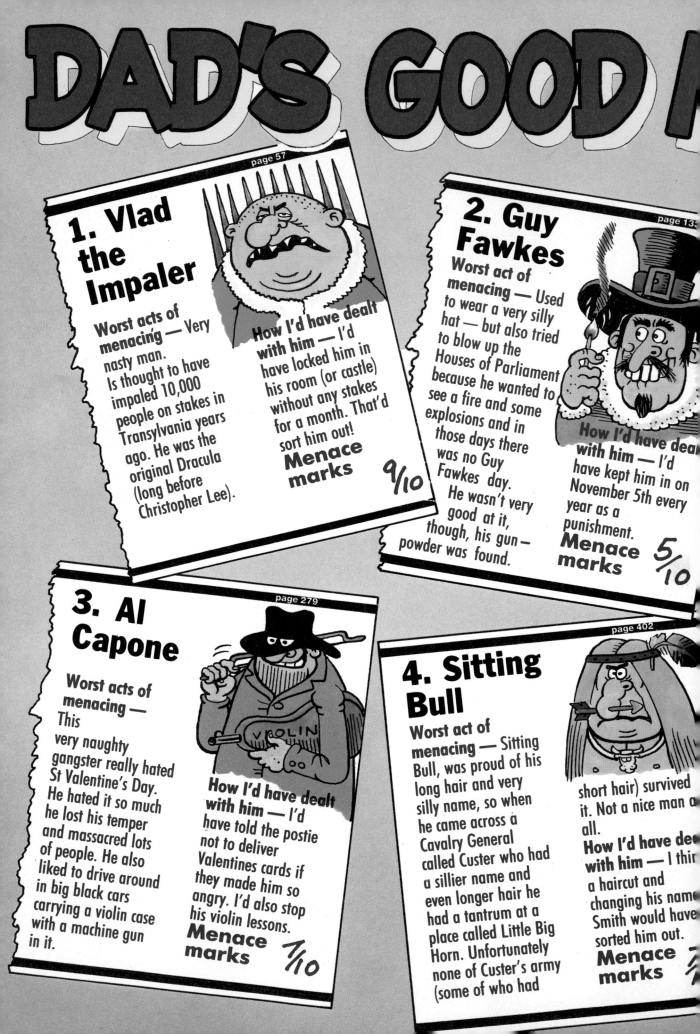

1. Vlad the Impaler

page 57

Worst acts of menacing — Very nasty man. Is thought to have impaled 10,000 people on stakes in Transylvania years ago. He was the original Dracula (long before Christopher Lee).

How I'd have dealt with him — I'd have locked him in his room (or castle) without any stakes for a month. That'd sort him out!

Menace marks 9/10

2. Guy Fawkes

page 133

Worst act of menacing — Used to wear a very silly hat — but also tried to blow up the Houses of Parliament because he wanted to see a fire and some explosions and in those days there was no Guy Fawkes day.

He wasn't very good at it, though, his gunpowder was found.

How I'd have dealt with him — I'd have kept him in on November 5th every year as a punishment.

Menace marks 5/10

3. Al Capone

page 279

Worst acts of menacing — This very naughty gangster really hated St Valentine's Day. He hated it so much he lost his temper and massacred lots of people. He also liked to drive around in big black cars carrying a violin case with a machine gun in it.

How I'd have dealt with him — I'd have told the postie not to deliver Valentines cards if they made him so angry. I'd also stop his violin lessons.

Menace marks 1/10

4. Sitting Bull

page 402

Worst act of menacing — Sitting Bull, was proud of his long hair and very silly name, so when he came across a Cavalry General called Custer who had a sillier name and even longer hair he had a tantrum at a place called Little Big Horn. Unfortunately none of Custer's army (some of who had short hair) survived it. Not a nice man a all.

How I'd have dea with him — I thir a haircut and changing his nam Smith would have sorted him out.

Menace marks

MENACE GUIDE

THE WORLD'S FOREMOST MENACE EXPERT TELLS HOW HE'D DEAL WITH SOME OF THE WORLD'S WORST MENACES

page 500

5. Dennis the Menace

Worst acts of menacing — Everything he does every day of the week. But some of the worst are: Dressing Walter the Softy as a lamb and selling him to a butcher, tying up three wrestlers in a knot so complicated that they still haven't been untied six months later, telling the whole crowd at the Cup Final that Walter's Mum had invited them round to tea — the poor woman ran out of teabags 742 times, telling Gnasher that I liked nothing better than having my leg chewed.

How I deal with him — I run away and hide.

Menace marks 10/10

CHILLY RECEPTION

HOW MUCH ARE THOSE DOGGIES IN THE WINDOW?

How much are those doggies in the
   window? (GNASH! GNASH!)
The ones with the black spiky hair.
   (GNIP! GNIP!)
How much are those doggies in the
   window?
Please name your price for the pair!

I've got an aardvark who plays the
   trumpet. (TOOT! TOOT!)
I've got a strange tap dancing shrew
   (TAP! TAP!)
I've got a sword swallowing gorilla.
Now all that I need are these two.

Their teeth are the finest in the kingdom. (SNAP! SNAP!)
Their fame it has spread through the land. (SPREAD! SPREAD!)
I love their adventures in "The Beano".
To own them would be mighty grand.

I'll give you a diamond studded cartie.
    (GLEAM! GLEAM!)
A catapult made of pure gold.
    (TWANG! TWANG!)
I'll give you a giant mound of ice cream,
If to me those doggies are sold.

I'll sell you those doggies in the window. (GASP! GASP!)
The ones with the black spiky hair. (WOW! WOW!)
They're stuffed ones made for me by my mother.
So where are the real ones? — right there!

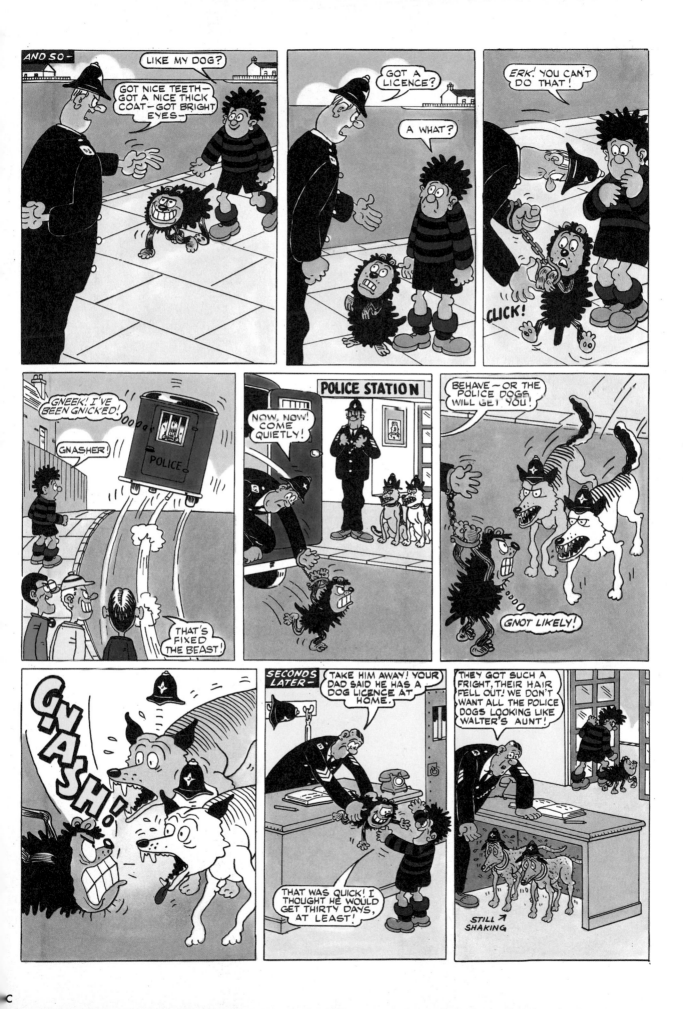

THAT'S SNOW BUSINESS!

OUCH! A BIG SNOWFLAKE!

CAREFUL, WALTER! ← READER'S VOICE

← PRINCE OF SOFTIES

LATER—

THE SNOW'S OFF NOW. WE CAN GET ON WITH OUR SNOWMAN.

ISN'T HE NICE?

MEANWHILE—

MAKE IT A BIG ONE, PALS!

AND—

OH, THIS REALLY IS A SUPER ONE, WALTER!

AND MEANWHILE—

GNICE!

FINISHED! YOU KNOW WHAT TO DO NOW, PALS!

GNEE! HEE!

BULL'S-EYE!

AARGH!

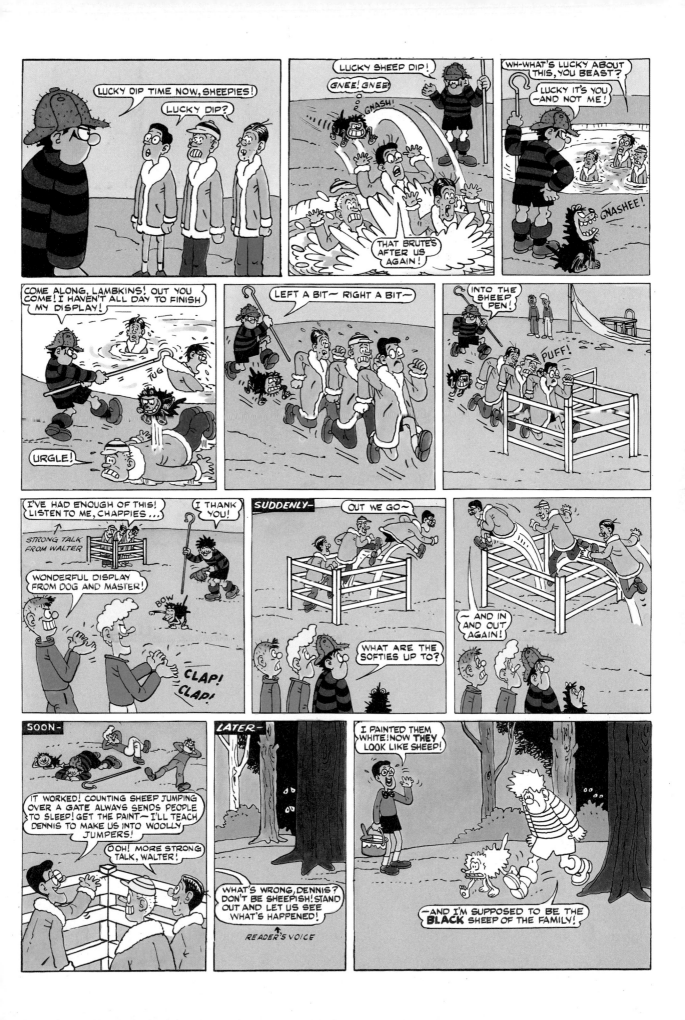

GREAT SPORTING MOMENTS

DENNIS IN THE BEANOTOWN GRAND PRIX

MAKE YOUR OWN MENACE

TO MAKE THIS GUARANTEED SOFTY SCARER YOU WILL NEED:—

10 toilet roll tubes
1 round cheese segment box
Red and black sticky paper (or paint)
Stiff card
Glue
Sticky tape
Scissors
Felt tip pens
Wool or string

HOW TO DO IT

1. Make sure no softies are watching.
2. Draw round cheese segment box onto a piece of card and draw Dennis's face onto it. Then cut it out. Make hair from black paper then stick the hair and face onto the box.
3. Make Dennis's body by rolling up a bit of cardboard 10 cm. tall. Cover one end with another piece of cardboard.
4. Fire catapult at your dad.
5. Make legs and arms by joining two toilet rolls together. Join the arms loosely with string and the legs stiffly with tape.
6. Add hands and feet. The hands are cut from cardboard. The feet are made from toilet rolls.
7. Thread string (or wool) through the length of the arms and legs and join the string to holes punched in the body. The string should be loose enough to allow the limbs to move.
8. Tie the head onto the piece of cardboard at the top of the body tube.
9. Attach strings to arms legs and head of the puppet and tie the other ends to a "T" bar for controlling the puppet.
10. Colour in the puppet with red and black sticky paper stripes for the jersey and shorts and felt tip pen for the face and hands.
11. Go menace a softy with it.

YOU WILL NEED

A large cardboard tube
Sticky black paper
Card for face and feet
4 smaller cardboard tubes for legs.

FOR ADDED SOFTY SCARING POWER —
The GNASHER PUPPET

1. Cover the body tube with bits of black paper to look like Gnasher's hair.
2. Draw the face on a bit of card and stick it onto one end of tube.
3. Colour leg tubes black and attach feet made of cut out cardboard to the ends.
4. Tie the legs onto holes punched in the body.
5. Stick a cardboard tail onto the rear of the body.
6. Attach a string to the puppet from a hole in the middle of its back.
7. Bite someone with it.

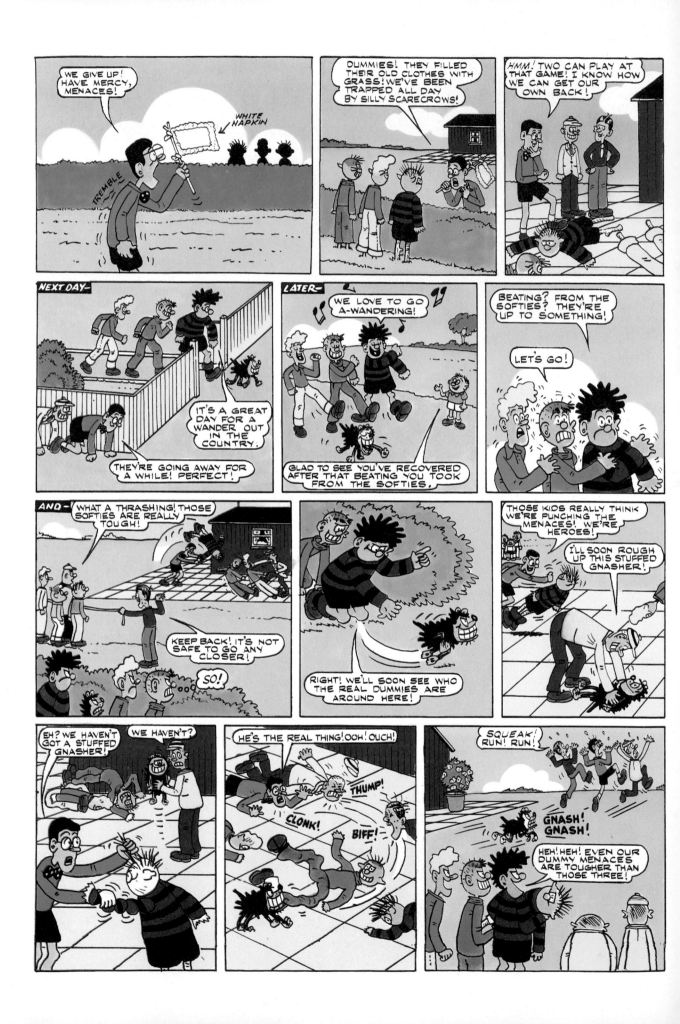

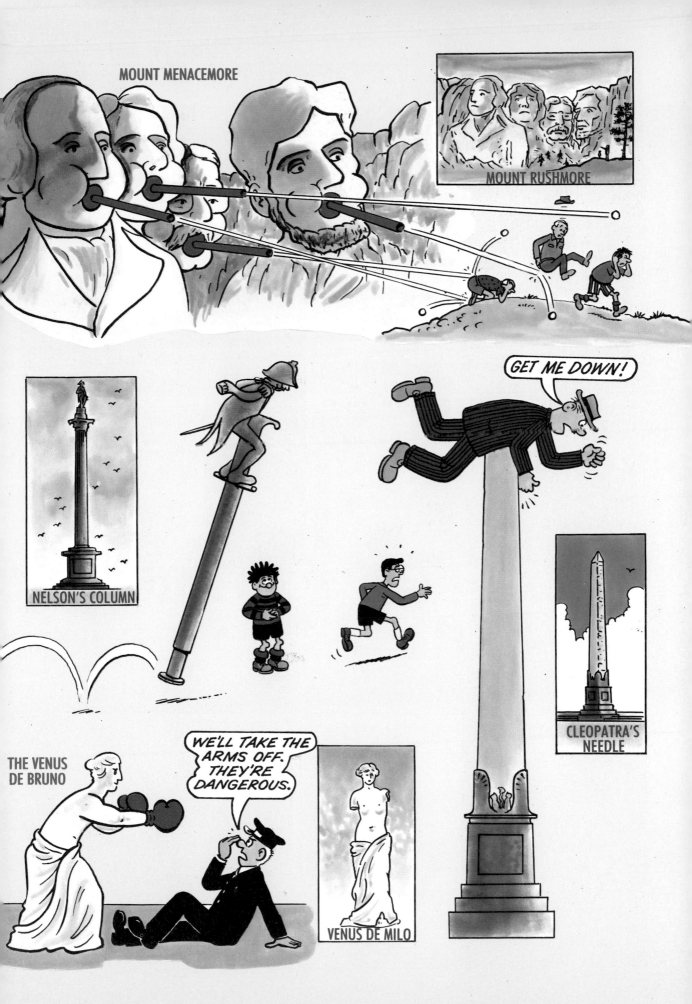

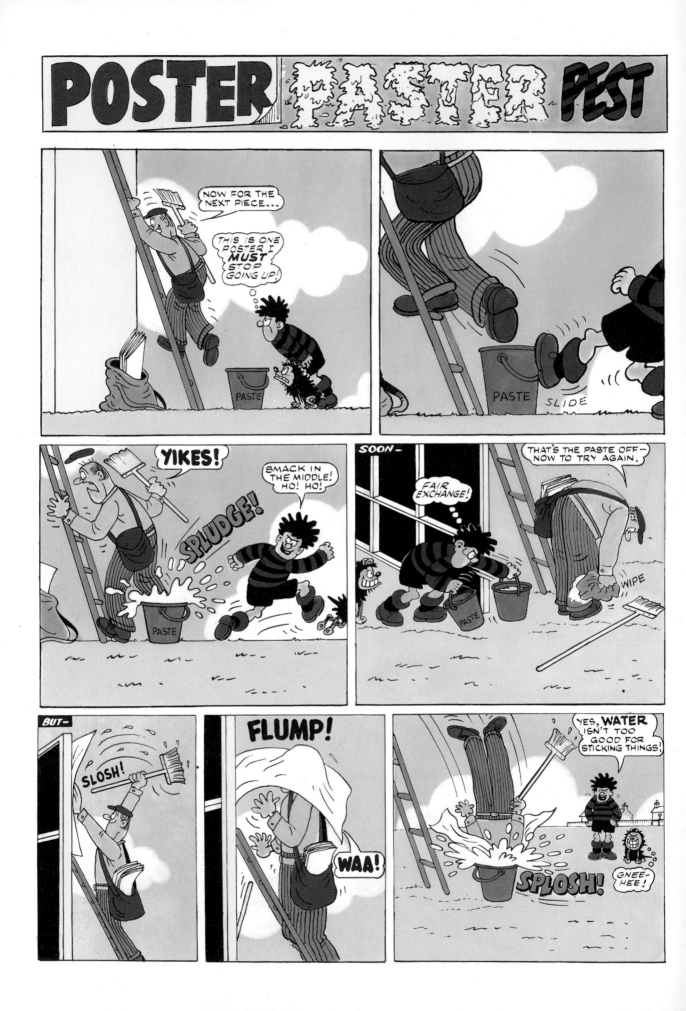

GREAT SPORTING MOMENTS

HOW DENNIS LED THE
TOUR DE BEANOTOWN